Color by Number

Use the code to color the picture.

1 one

  Count and color the one hippo.

Color 1.

  Trace and write the numeral.

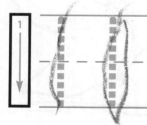

2 two

  Count and color the two clowns.

Color 2.

  Trace and write the numeral.

2 2 2

3 **three**

  Count and color the three toys.

Color 3.

Trace and write the numeral.

3

 four

 Count and color the four sweaters.

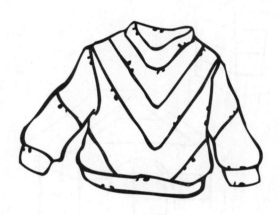

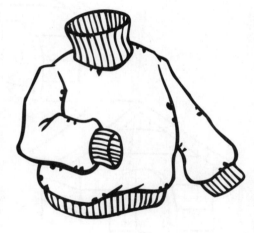

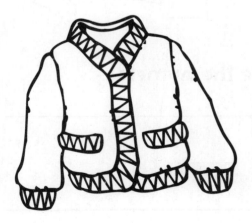

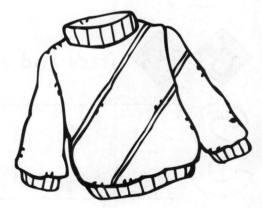

Color 4.

  Trace and write the numeral.

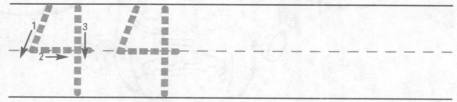

9

5 **five**

Count and color the
five jack-o-lanterns.

Color 5.

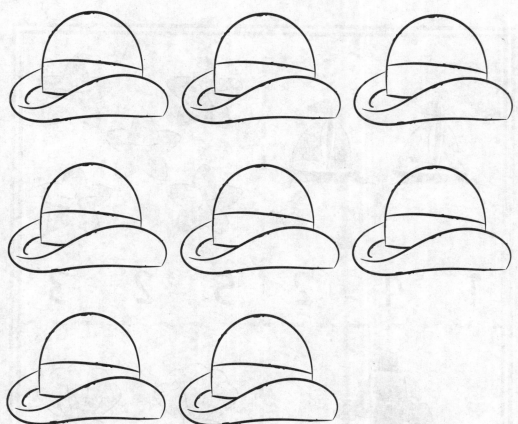

  Trace and write the numeral.

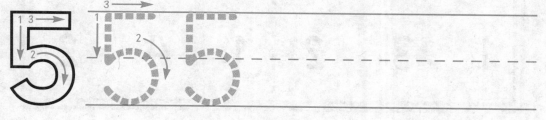

Count the objects.
Circle the correct number.

1   4   2   5   2   3

1   3   2   1   4   2

Count the objects.
Write the correct number.

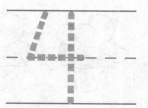

Count the objects. Draw a line to the correct number to show how many.

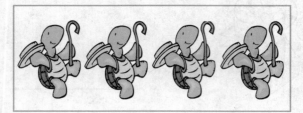

Use the code to color the picture.

1 =   2 =   3 =   4 =

15

 **six**

  Count and color the six dogs.

Color 6.

  Trace and write the numeral.

 **seven**

Count and color the seven grasshoppers.

Color 7.

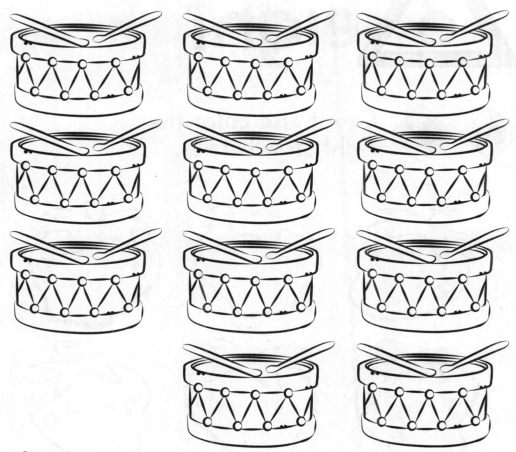

  Trace and write the numeral.

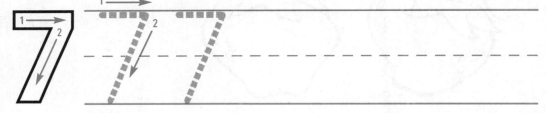

8 eight

  Count and color the eight strawberries.

Color 8.

  Trace and write the numeral.

 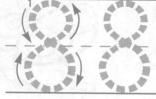

 21

9 nine

  Count and color the nine butterflies.

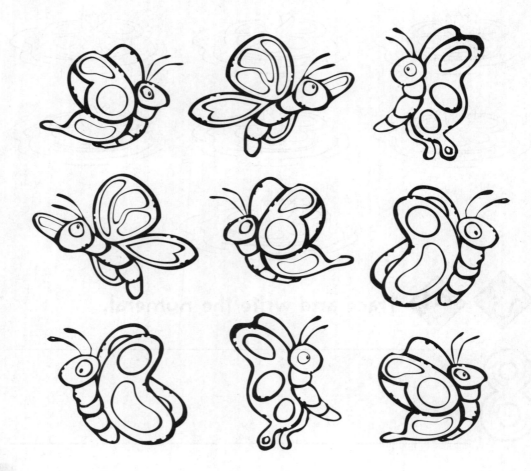

Color 9.

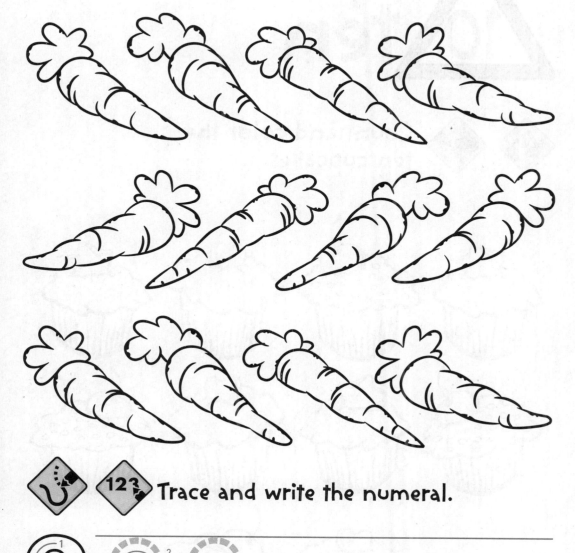

Trace and write the numeral.

 **ten**

Count and color the ten cupcakes.

Color 10.

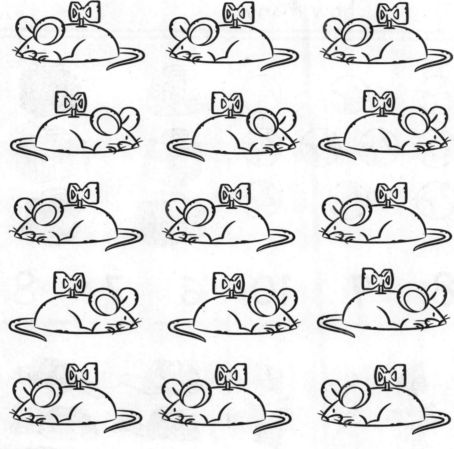

  Trace and write the numeral.

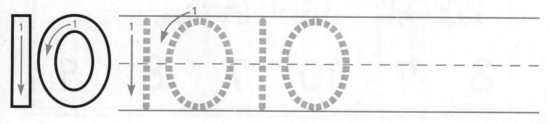

Count the objects. Circle the correct number to show how many.

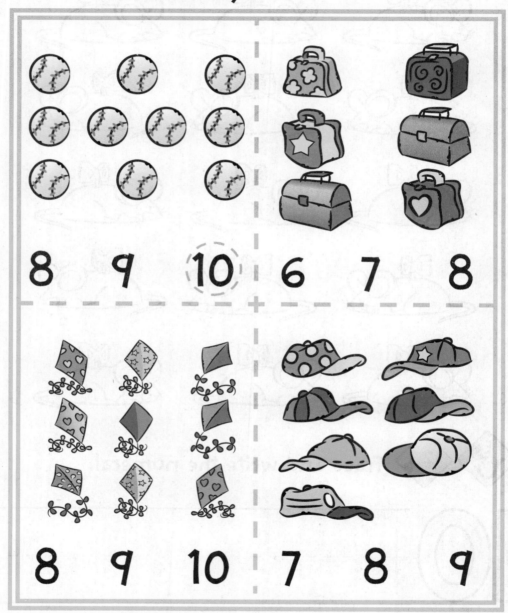

8 9 (10) 6 7 8

8 9 10 7 8 9

Count the objects. Write the correct number to show how many.

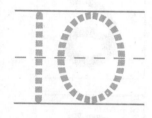

27

Count the objects. Draw a line to the correct number to show how many.

6

9

7

8

10

 **Connect the dots from 1 to 10. Color the picture.**

 Write your phone number.

My phone number is

_____

- -

_____

Color to show the number.

4

9

5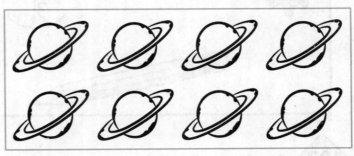

8

123 Write the numerals 1 to 10.

1   3   5

6   10

123 Write the numerals 10 to 1.

10   9   6

5

31

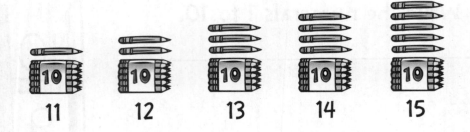

11   12   13   14   15

 Count the objects. Write the correct number to show how many.

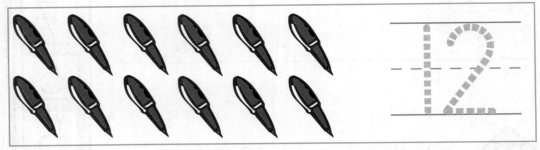

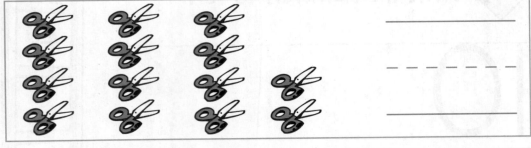

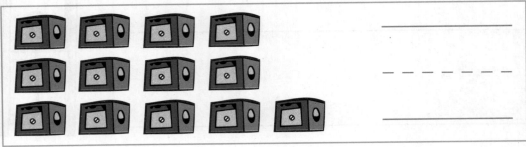

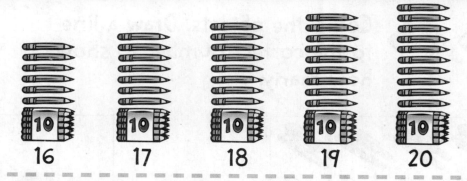

16   17   18   19   20

 Count the objects. Write the correct number to show how many.

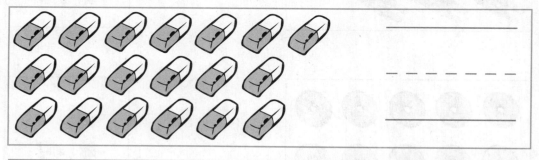

_____

- - - - - - - - - - -

_____

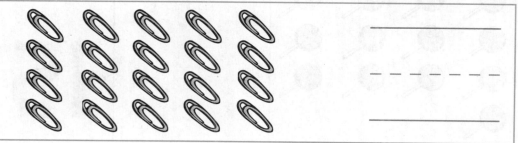

_____

- - - - - - - - - - -

_____

33

Count the objects. Draw a line to the correct number to show how many.

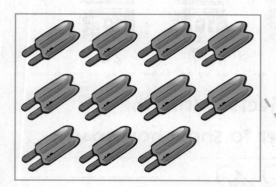

13

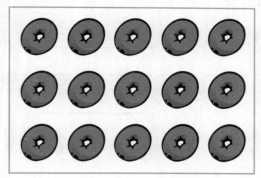

11

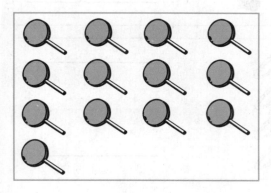

15

Count the objects. Draw a line to the correct number to show how many.

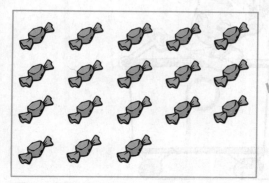

20

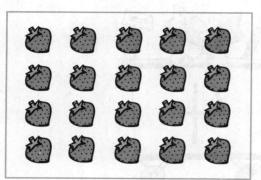

17

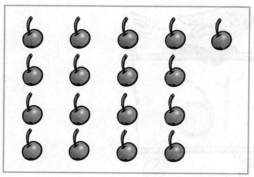

18

35

Write the number that comes before.

123 Write the number that comes before.

Write the number that comes after.

6   7

10   _____

14   _____

Write the number that comes after.

1 ____

16 ____

8 ____

Write the number that comes between.

4

_3_

2

15

_ _ _

13

11

_ _ _

9

Clown Fun

 Connect the dots from 1 to 20.
Color the picture.

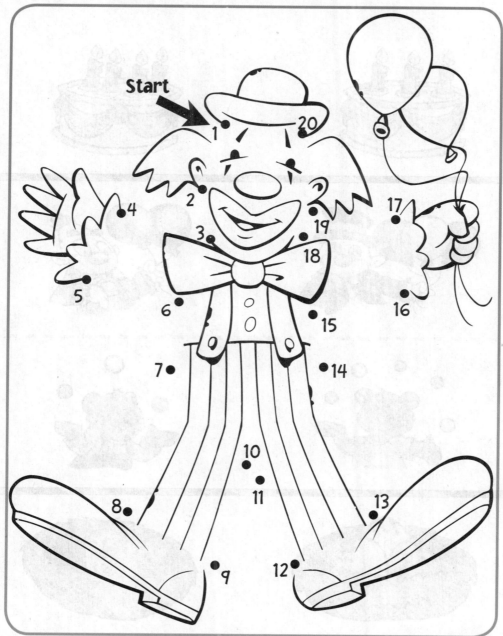

Count the objects.
Circle the picture with more.

Count the objects.
Circle the group with fewer objects.

Draw one more. Write the number to show how many.

Show one fewer. Write the number to show how many.

Same Amount

  Draw a line between the ones with the same amount.

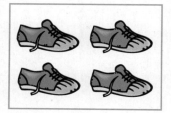

Trace each shape.

square

circle

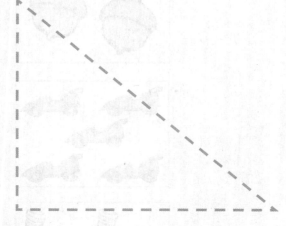

triangle

rectangle

Write **S** on all squares.
Write **T** on all triangles.

 Write **C** on all circles.
Write **R** on all rectangles.

Draw a line between the matching shapes.

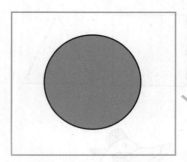

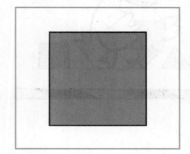

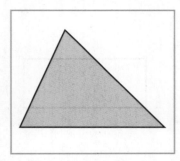

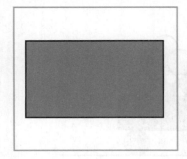

Count the shapes.
Write how many.

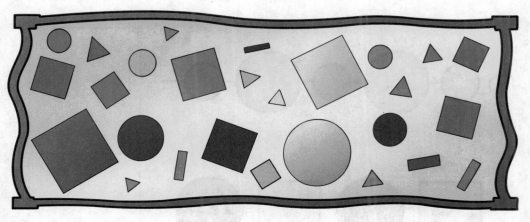

How many ⬜ s? _____

How many △ s? _____

How many ◯ s? _____

How many ▭ s? _____

49

Draw and color the shape that comes next.

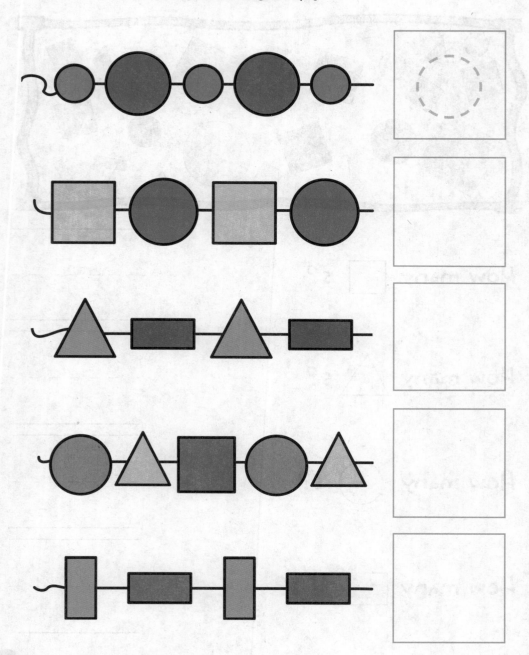

What's the Same?

Circle the shape that is the same.

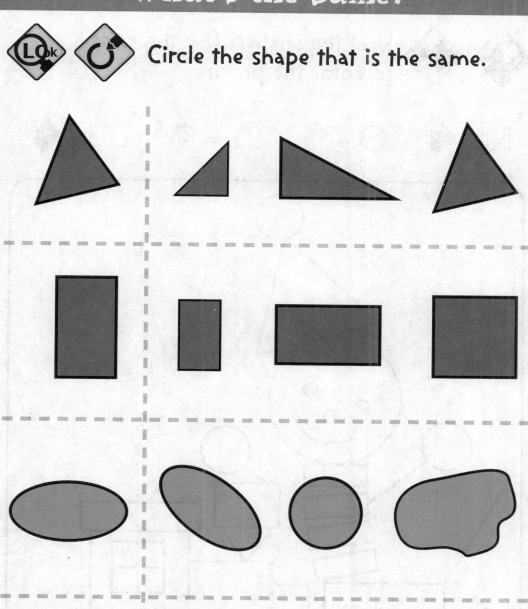

Find the shapes. Use the code to color the picture.

   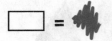

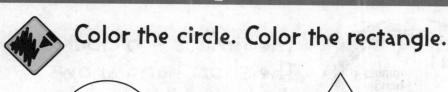 Color the circle. Color the rectangle.

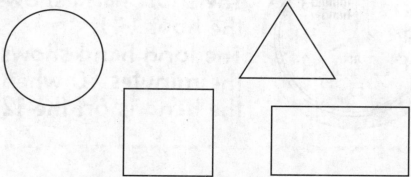

 Continue the pattern.

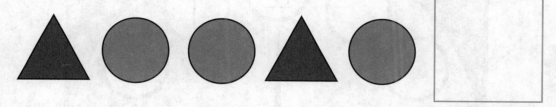

 Circle the shape that is the same.

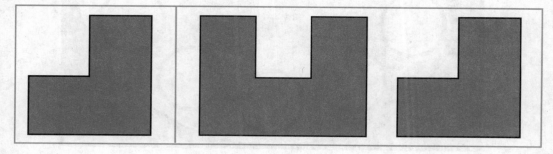

The time is 4 o'clock.
The short hand shows the hour (4).
The long hand shows the minutes (0 when the hand is on the 12).

 Write the clock numbers.

4 o'clock   **4:00**

  Draw a line beween the
clocks with the same time.

Write the time.

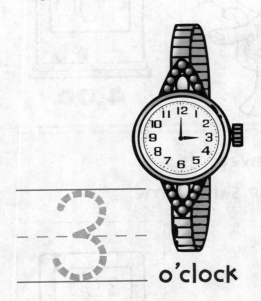

3

_____ o'clock

_____ o'clock

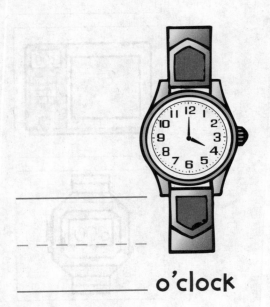

_____ o'clock

_____ o'clock

Write the digital time on the clocks.

taller   **shorter**

Color the taller tree.
Circle the shorter tree.

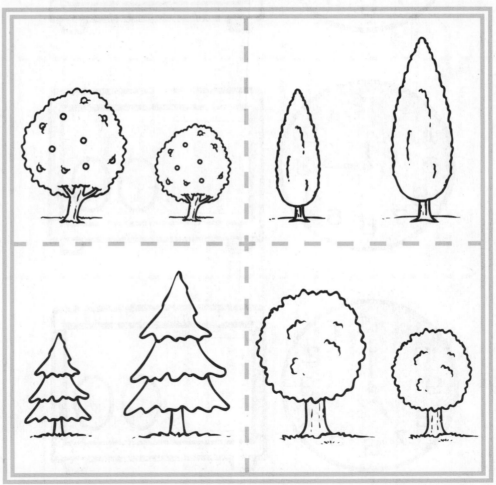

shorter　　　　　　　　　　longer

 Color the longer collar.

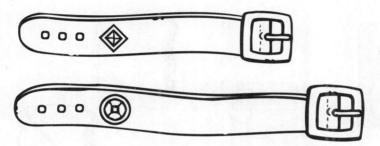

 Color the dog with the shorter nose.

2 equal parts

2 parts not equal

 Circle the pictures that show 2 equal parts.

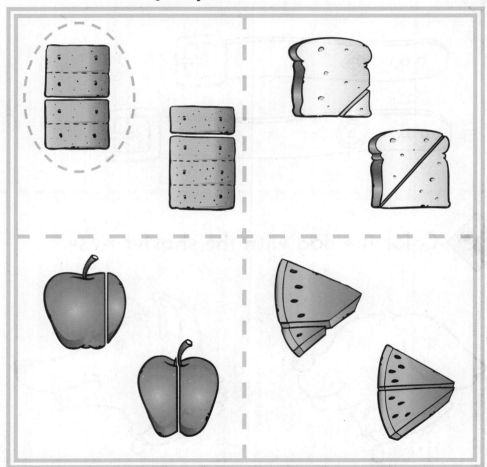

$$\frac{1 \text{ part shaded}}{2 \text{ equal parts}}$$

1/2 or one half is shaded.

Two equal parts are halves.

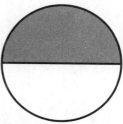

  Circle the shapes that show halves. Color 1/2 of each shape.

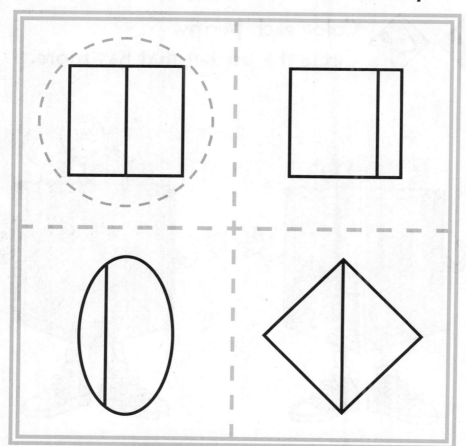

61

This is a penny.
A penny has two sides.

heads   tails

 Color each penny.
Circle the pocket that has more.

= 4¢

  Count the pennies.
Write how many cents.

   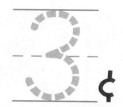 ¢

    ¢

    ¢

Penny Jars

Draw lines to match the pennies with the correct jars.

1¢

2¢

3¢

5¢

7¢

9¢

64